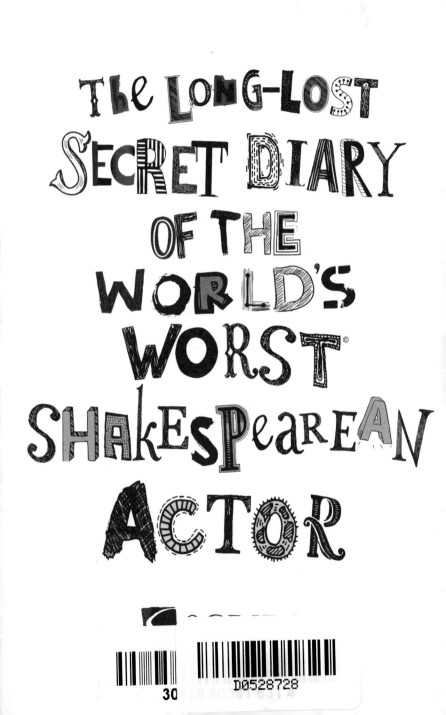

THE LONG-LOST SECRET DIARY OF THE WORLD'S WORST SHAKESPEAREAN ACTOR

First published in Great Britain by Scribo MMXX
Scribo, an imprint of
The Salariya Book Company
25 Marlborough Place, Brighton, BN1 1UB

ISBN 978-1-912904-23-5

Book design by David Salariya

Printed and bound in China

The text for this book is set in Century Schoolbook
The display type is Jacob Riley

www.salariya.com

Illustrations: Isobel Lundie

THE LONG-LOST SECRET DIARY OF THE WORLD'S WORST SHAKESPEAREAN ACTOR

Written by
Tim Collins

Illustrated by
Isobel Lundie

SCRIBO
a SALARIYA *imprint*

DISCLAIMER

This book features characters collecting dog poo for use in tanning leather. Please don't try this at home (or outside your home either!) – handling dog poo can be very dangerous, especially for children!

Chapter I

London
1603

Saturday 1ˢᵗ February

My friend Spud came round today and asked if I wanted to go to the Globe Theatre. Spud loves plays, and he's seen a lot because he wants to be an actor one day. But I've never been to one.

Usually I ask Mother and she refuses. But today she was out collecting dog poo with my brother Philip, so I asked Father instead. He was concentrating so much on stitching some pieces of leather that he gave me a penny without thinking about it.

It's enough to buy a loaf of bread, as Mother always tells me. But I don't care if I have to go without food for a week. I need to see what all the fuss is about.

I always see big crowds flocking to the Globe to see The Lord Chamberlain's Men performing William Shakespeare's plays.

They're meant to be the best playing company in London, and living so close without being able to watch them has been awful.

But that all changes tomorrow afternoon. We'll be going to see something called *A Midsummer Night's Dream*. Can't wait.

Sunday 2nd February

Mother kept asking me what I was planning to do this morning, and I had to change the subject every time to avoid mentioning the theatre or the penny Father gave me.

I tried to distract her by offering to help her prepare some leather, but this just made her suspicious. I never volunteer to help, because I find it really disgusting.

Father makes shoes, and Mother and Philip help him out by treating the leather. First they soak it in a mixture of salt, lime and wee. Then comes the really horrible part when they wash it with a solution with dog poo in it to make it more flexible.

Mother spent the whole time shouting at me for doing it wrong, while Philip kept boasting about the excellent quality of the dog poo they'd found.

This is a good one!

GET REAL

Tanners would use mixtures of lime and urine to remove hair from leather they were treating. They would then wash the leather in a solution that might contain dog poo or pigeon droppings to remove the lime and soften up the leather, making it more flexible.

I managed to slip away just after noon, and I made my way to Spud's house. His father is a schoolmaster, and he thinks Spud is going to follow in his footsteps. Every night Spud goes up to his room and pretends to read his Latin grammar book, but really he gets out his collection of speeches and acts them out. He writes them down from memory every time he goes to see a play, and he has a whole stack of them now.

We made our way to the Globe, and Spud told me about it on the way. He said it would be noisy and crowded, but I still wasn't prepared for what it was actually like.

Every inch of the huge, round wooden building was crammed. Spud said there were over three thousand people in total. Some had paid a penny to stand on the floor like us, while others had paid more to sit in high galleries.

People were wandering around selling apples, oranges, nuts and gingerbread. I wouldn't have bought anything even if I'd had the money because it was all so overpriced. You can get the same stuff from the market for half of what they were asking.

Everyone around us chatted as we waited for the play to start. We had to move because there was a man with a loud voice who'd seen the play before, and he kept telling his friend what was going to happen. It didn't occur to him that people who'd just paid to see it might not want the ending spoiled.

Soon a thin man on a high balcony blew a trumpet and it was time for the play to start.

Toot!

Watch where you're pointing that thing!

Everyone crushed forward, and my feet got stamped on, which really hurt. You'd think having a shoemaker for a father would mean I could at least rely on solid footwear, but he only lets me have the ones that aren't good enough to sell, and my current shoes are far too big with massive holes in them.

I found a good spot where I could see the stage and stuck to it the whole time. A man with a feather in his hat stood in front of me at one point, and I had to pluck it out so I could see better.

The play was really good, and I can see why so many people like the theatre. It was about some people who go to a wedding and meet fairies. The funniest character was called Bottom, and the best bit was when a fairy called Puck transformed him into a donkey and made

Titania fall in love with him. The crowd were laughing so much I could hardly hear what the actors were saying.

Unsurprisingly, I was in trouble with Mother when I got home. I tried to sneak upstairs, but she dragged me down and yelled at me for going out and enjoying myself while everyone else was working hard.

Mother always goes really red when she's telling me off. Her straggly black hair shakes back and forth as she fixes her dark eyes on me and jabs her stained fingers in the air.

I feel worse if Father shouts at me, because that hardly ever happens. But he didn't say a word today. He just examined a piece of leather while Mother ranted. I think he's in trouble too for handing over the penny.

Oh well. It doesn't look like I'll ever be going back to the theatre. But at least I went once.

GET REAL

In Shakespeare's day, plays always ended with a 'jig' where the actors danced to music. Nowadays, plays usually just end with the curtains going down and the house lights going up, which is obviously much less exciting.

Monday 3rd February

I spent most of today outside our house going through the best bits from *A Midsummer Night's Dream* with Spud. He kept acting chunks out, while I cheered and shouted like a noisy spectator. William Shakespeare must be good at thinking up lines that stick in your head, because lines from the play keep coming back to me. But even so, I was impressed by how much Spud had managed to remember.

I hope Spud gets to become an actor, but it's not something I ever want to try. It makes my legs feel weak just thinking about standing in front of a packed theatre and reciting lines.

The 'groundlings' who cluster around the stage will throw nutshells, apple cores and whatever stinky leftovers they can grab if they don't like a performance. Spud says if they really hate you, they go out to the baiting pits to find some dead dogs to throw, but I'm not sure I believe that.

I don't really like standing around outside our house, but I've got nowhere else to go. We live on a narrow street lined with small houses crowded with noisy families. It's clogged with mud, firewood and horse dung, and every now and then a window will open and washing water or wee from a chamber pot will be tossed out.

Mother and Philip throw all their stuff for treating leather right out the front window when they've used it, so the bit outside our house is especially smelly.

I'd much rather go and look at the heads on London Bridge, but Mother says it's not safe to wander around on this side of the river, so she makes me stay nearby.

GET REAL

In the Elizabethan era, the heads of traitors were placed on spikes on top of the stone gateway to London Bridge. It was a tradition that dated back to the 14th century, and the heads of well-known people such as William Wallace and Thomas Cromwell had been placed there. The heads were dipped in tar to preserve them, however, so it might have been difficult to pick out the famous ones.

Tuesday 4ᵗʰ February

Spud has found out that the manager of
the Lord Chamberlain's Men, who's called
Lawrence, is looking for some young actors
to play small roles. He really wants to be
picked, and he's asked me to go along with him
tomorrow and tell Lawrence about what a great
actor he is.

He's written a speech that I'm going to
memorise, all about how he can reduce me
to tears with just one line of a tragedy, and
how I laughed so much at one of his comic
performances that I almost died and had to
stay in bed for three days.

I'm currently trying to learn it by the light of my
candle, and Philip is moaning that I'm muttering
too loudly. He has no right to complain after all
the times he's kept me awake telling me about
all the brilliant dog poo he's found.

I don't care anyway. This is Spud's big chance to get into acting. If Philip has a disturbed night, it's a small price to pay.

Wednesday 5th February

Okay, so that was a surprise. We went along to the door of the Globe to find that it was completely surrounded by boys our age. They were all jostling each other out of the way, and jumping up with their hands in the air to get Lawrence's attention.

Lawrence had thinning grey hair and was wearing a tight red jacket with a frilly collar, purple breeches that went to just below his knees, and white stockings. He looked at each of the boys, stroked his chin and crumpled his face, as if deep in thought.

Spud shoved me to the front and told me to give the speech. I had to shout really loudly to be heard above the others.

Lawrence pointed at me and said 'Yes!'

I couldn't stop myself grinning. Not only had I managed to remember my speech, but it had been enough to convince the manager of the Lord Chamberlain's Men to give my friend a role.

I stepped aside, so Spud could get through.

Lawrence shook his head. He said he wanted me, not Spud. He said my voice was loud and clear, and that I'd make a good fairy with my blond hair and delicate looks.

Some of the other boys sniggered at this, but Spud didn't smile. He just sighed and his shoulders drooped.

I tried to explain that I'd only come to help Spud and I didn't really want to be an actor because people would throw dead dogs at me. Lawrence thrust his arms about and launched into a speech about how I was being given a chance to work alongside the greatest players of the age and I should not pass it up lightly.

I found myself saying 'yes'. I still wasn't keen about going on stage, but I thought it would at least stop Mother telling me to help out more.

When Father's brother Samuel died of the ague, he left me some money to go to school, and things have been tough since I left. I feel like I should be doing something better than helping Mother and Philip now I can read and write, but I don't know what. It just seems like all my learning will have been wasted if I end up chasing dogs to steal their poo.

I know acting isn't the thing I want to do, but at least it might keep Mother quiet if I tell her I've been chosen to do to something. And I'd much rather spend my days at the Globe than standing outside our house.

Lawrence said I'd be playing one of the fairy attendants in *A Midsummer Night's Dream*. I felt myself panicking as I wondered what I'd let myself in for. But then I thought back to the play, and the only fairy attendants I could remember were four boys who briefly hung around Queen Titania. I could barely remember them speaking, so they must have been very small roles. It was fine. I could cope. I felt my breathing go back to normal.

Spud was okay about me getting chosen instead of him. He said he was sure a role that was right for him would come up soon, and I promised to mention him whenever Lawrence was looking.

Mother and Father weren't so happy, of course. They said I shouldn't be wasting my time pretending to be a woman in made-up stories when I could learn something useful like treating leather or making shoes.

But I think plays are as useful as shoes in their own way. They help you forget all about plagues and wars and religious squabbles for a few hours, and that's something we all need.

GET REAL

Women weren't allowed to act in the Elizabethan theatre, so female roles were played by boys instead. Elaborate costumes including corsets and large frames made out of cane called 'farthingales' were used to alter their appearance.

Chapter 2
An actor's life

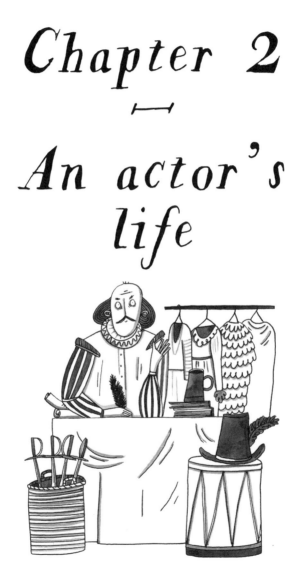

Thursday 6th February

That wasn't too bad, I suppose. I arrived at
the Globe this morning to find the other actors
studying piles of paper with their parts written
on. I was handed a small scrap with my four
lines on:

And I
Hail
Cobweb
Ready

I had been cast as a fairy called Cobweb, and I memorised my lines, and my 'cues', which are the ones that come before them so you know when to speak.

After that, I wandered around and watched the other actors. I spotted the one who'd played Bottom, who's called Edward in real life. I told him he'd really made me laugh when he turned into a donkey, but instead of thanking me he launched into the scene again, repeating his lines a few different ways and asking me which performance was best. I thought they were all good, but I picked one anyway just to make him stop.

Then another actor called Nicholas hurried over, barged in front of Edward, cleared his throat and recited a speech from a different play called *Henry V*. It began, 'Once more unto the breach, dear friends', and went on for ages.

I couldn't work out why he was doing it at first, but then I realised he must be so vain that he can't bear to see anyone being praised for their acting without jumping in and grabbing some attention for himself.

I told him how brilliant his performance was over and over again until finally he stopped.

I took refuge from these attention-hungry actors by heading backstage. I was expecting to find a massive area full of props, costumes and free food, but instead there was just a small room called a 'tiring house'. The thin man I'd seen with the trumpet, who's called Anthony, was flapping around and arranging piles of clothing. He was just as dramatic as the actors, even though he wasn't on stage. He was wailing about how Lawrence never gave him time to prepare, and kept changing his mind about which plays they were going to do.

29

He got even more stressed when all the actors crammed into the small room to change into their costumes. I was handed a pair of wings and some flowers for my hair, but most actors had more elaborate clothes. The man playing Titania had to wear a corset and a hooped cage to go under his huge white dress.

Lawrence barged in and announced we had another good crowd. I started to worry about what would happen if I forgot one of my four lines in front of so many people. Maybe I'd be the first fairy attendant ever to be booed off.

I felt my hands trembling, and for the first time in my life I thought that maybe collecting dog poo wouldn't be so bad. At least people wouldn't shout angrily at me, unless I tried to shake hands with them afterwards.

I was ready to give up and run home, but I forced myself to go on stage. And it turned out not to be so bad. There were three other fairy attendants, and all I had to do was follow them around and say my lines with them.

I could tell my voice was cracking and my legs were shaking, but I'm pretty sure nobody threw any dead dogs, cats or bears. I'd have noticed that.

After the play was over, Lawrence ran over and said I'd done a wonderful job. He clasped his hands together and praised the way I'd used a high voice to show I was a female fairy. I nodded as if I'd done it on purpose.

He said he'd been right to spot my talent, and invited me to come back tomorrow for another role. I really hope I don't have more than four lines this time.

GET REAL

Rather than large backstage areas, Elizabethan theatres had a small space called the 'tiring house'. This was because it was where the actors put on their costumes, or 'attire'. Plays in Elizabethan England didn't use much scenery, but costumes were an important part of the show. They could be very expensive, and actors would be heavily fined if they left the theatre with them on.

Friday 7th February

When I got to the theatre this morning, Lawrence said we were doing a play called *Henry VI Part I*. I played a porter, and all I had to say was 'Madam, I will' and hand over some keys, so it was an even smaller role than last time.

It didn't take me long to remember the part, so I had plenty of time to wander around.

I went into the tiring house and saw a bald man with a beard sitting behind a small desk.

I assumed he was some sort of assistant and asked if he could show me which costume I needed. It was only when I saw he was scribbling on a sheet of paper that I realised who he was. This was William Shakespeare, the man who writes the plays.

Spud once told me that most playwrights are dodgy characters who spend their time drinking and fighting. One of them, Christopher Marlowe, was even killed in a fight over who should pay a bill. But Shakespeare seemed pretty normal.

He told me about a new play he's working on called *Measure for Measure*, in which a duke disguises himself as a friar and lets his strict deputy take over. It didn't sound as exciting as *A Midsummer Night's Dream*, so I suggested that he include a scene in which the duke turns someone into a donkey. He said he'd consider it.

Before long, all the other actors were crowding into the room and it was time for Anthony to run upstairs and blast his trumpet.

I still got a weird feeling in my stomach when I stepped onto the stage, but at least it was over quickly this time.

I must have done okay, because Lawrence wants me to play the Hostess in *The Taming of the Shrew* next. It doesn't sound that bad, because I've only got three lines and they're all at the very start, which means I'll be able to enjoy the rest of the play afterwards.

GET REAL

Playwrights were not well respected in Elizabethan England, and they had a reputation for bad behaviour. Christopher Marlowe was the most successful playwright before Shakespeare, but he was known as a violent and dangerous man. He died at the age of just 29 after being stabbed in a fight about the payment of a bill. Some believe he was really assassinated, but the truth may never be known.

Saturday 8ᵗʰ February

That seemed to go okay. I played a hostess from an alehouse who was angry with a man called Christopher Sly. The crowd kept on being rowdy even after Anthony had blown the trumpet, so I had to shout really loudly.

Quite a few people in the audience laughed, and Edward, who was playing Christopher Sly, went along with it by pulling a funny face and covering his ears as if to protect them from the noise.

The crowd paid much more attention to the play after that, so I think we did a good job of settling them. But Edward seemed angry when we got back to the tiring house. He said they were an ignorant rabble who didn't deserve our talent, and Lawrence should get us a better class of customer.

I think he should be pleased we have a crowd at all. Without them we'd just be a random bunch of people pretending to be kings and fairies.

Edward had some other roles in the play, but I was free to sneak up to the gallery above the stage and watch the rest of it.

It was about a man called Petruchio who marries a woman called Katherine even though she's really rude. She changes and becomes obedient towards the end, but I preferred her at the start. There were loads of good jokes in it, and the crowd loved it.

Sunday 9ᵗʰ February

Lawrence said that my family could come along to see a play for free if they liked, but they weren't interested.

I thought Mother might enjoy shouting at some actors instead of us for a couple of hours, but she said she didn't care about made-up stories. Philip said his rivals would beat him to the best dog poo if he wasted an afternoon in a theatre. And Father said plays sounded boring, but he'd be interested if I could get him into one of the cockfighting shows for free instead.

Cockfighting? Who wants to see two stupid birds pecking each other when you could enjoy a great story? In the theatre, we can take you to faraway places or the distant past. With just a few props and the right words from Shakespeare, we can make you laugh, cry, gasp and hiss. And Father would rather watch a couple of angry chickens? He's crazy.

Oh. I just realised I wrote 'we' in that last bit, like I'm part of the company. I'm not. I'm just playing a few small roles and I don't even know how long I'll be doing it for.

GET REAL

The Globe Theatre was built on the south bank of the Thames, in an area known for rowdy entertainment. As well as watching a play, you could gamble and watch cruel sports like bear-baiting, where dogs would attack a bear that was chained to a post, and cockfighting, where cockerels would fight to the death.

Monday 10th February

How odd. Just last night I was writing about how silly it is to think I was part of the Lord Chamberlain's Men, and now I am. Sort of.

Lawrence said he'd been impressed by my acting so far, and he'd like me to join the company as an apprentice.

I agreed at once. There's no way Mother can force me to collect dog poo with Philip if I'm an apprentice.

Lawrence said he couldn't pay me, but he'd give me food in exchange for performing minor roles and helping out with a few little jobs. He also said I shouldn't get carried away and expect to be playing Julius Caesar by next week.

That's fine by me. I don't want big roles anyway. It would be terrifying to have to learn all those lines and perform them in front of massive crowds.

Mother and Father weren't pleased about my news at first, but they lightened up when I explained I'd be getting my food for free. They forgot all about the theatre and started to work out how much extra food they could afford for themselves.

GET REAL

Diet in Elizabethan England depended on social class. Rich people could regularly afford meat such as beef, pork and mutton, as well as fruit and vegetables. The poor had much less variety, and most meals would consist of bread with butter, cheese and soup.

Chapter 3

⊢━━⊣

Stage fright

Tuesday IIth February

Those 'few little jobs' Lawrence mentioned
turned out to be hours of back-breaking labour.
I had to sweep the tiring house and every single
one of the galleries this morning. Then I had
to carry heavy loads of costumes up from the
storage space under the stage.

And as for the food, it turned out to be nothing
more than a chunk of stale bread. To make it
worse, Lawrence sent me out to buy meat pies
for himself, Anthony and Shakespeare and I
didn't even get any of the leftovers.

I got back to discover that Mother, Father
and Philip had already treated themselves to
a delicious pig's head from the local butcher's
stall. I asked if I could have one of the ears, but
they said they wanted to make it last, and I was
getting food from my fancy actor friends now.

This is awful. Everyone is eating better than me, even Philip. And he uses the same napkin to clean his knife that he uses to wipe his poo-collecting shovel, so good food is wasted on him.

Wednesday 12th February

I spent the whole morning tidying up the tiring house. Shakespeare was sitting at his desk, scribbling on a thick piece of paper. I hoped he might help, but he was too distracted by his work. I'm sure it's all very important, but he could at least have offered.

Shakespeare was in a complete daze and Lawrence had to snap his fingers in front of his face to see if he wanted a pie. I was then sent out to buy a mincemeat pie and had to watch Shakespeare devour the whole thing without taking his eyes from his paper.

I met Spud on the way home and told him all about the hard work I've had to do. He said he was still jealous, because I get to be in the theatre all day. I don't think he really understands. Theatres might be exciting places while plays are on, but there's nothing exciting about clearing apple cores and nutshells out of the pit for three hours.

Spud is so determined to become an actor that he offered to come along and help me with my chores in the hope that Lawrence would spot him and give him a role. I couldn't bring myself to take advantage of him, but I promised I'd keep looking for a way to get him into one of the plays.

Thursday 13ᵗʰ February

I got bored sweeping the tiring house this
afternoon so I snapped my fingers in front of
Shakespeare's face and asked him what he was
writing. He said it was a play called *King Lear*
and that it's about a man who goes mad when
he's betrayed by his daughters.

It all sounded very gloomy. I remembered
Katherine in *The Taming of the Shrew*, so I
suggested he make it funnier by giving King
Lear an angry wife who tells him off all the
time. Shakespeare said that it was important
to the plot that King Lear's wife was dead
from the start. Fine. I was only trying to make
it better.

I asked Shakespeare why he was being
so touchy. It turns out he's worried that a
playwright called Ben Jonson is writing better
plays than him, so he's trying to make the new

ones really good. He keeps being woken up by the sound of boys outside his window discussing how great Jonson and his playing company The Admiral's Men are, and it's making him a bit sensitive.

I told Shakespeare that everyone loves his plays, especially the funny ones. After all his success, you'd think he'd be a little more confident. Writers must be as desperate for praise as actors.

GET REAL

Ben Jonson (1572–1637) wrote plays such as Volpone, The Alchemist *and* Bartholomew Fair. *When Shakespeare died, Jonson wrote that 'He was not of an age but for all time', which turned out to be right. The two writers seem to have been friends, but there may also have been some rivalry between them.*

Friday 14th February

The company are doing a play called *Hamlet* tomorrow. It's one of Shakespeare's newer ones, and it's very long, so everyone is trying to learn their parts. Luckily, Lawrence didn't give me a role this time.

Nicholas is playing Hamlet, and he was wandering around with a huge stack of papers and looking for someone to test him on his lines.

He cornered me in the tiring house and I had to listen to him reciting the speech that starts, 'O that this too too solid flesh would melt'.

It was so loud I found myself cowering. I know Nicholas needs to speak at full volume when he's out on the stage, but there was no need in that tiny room.

Nicholas went through the speech over and over again, and I thought it was really good every time. But whenever he finished, he'd throw his papers to the floor and say he was doing it all wrong and the crowd would hate it.

I had to keep telling him he was a brilliant actor and it would all be fine. It was quite a relief when Lawrence grabbed me to do my chores. Even sweeping the galleries is better than pandering to the star actors.

I was quite enjoying the peace and quiet of sweeping for once, but Lawrence gave me a painful new job instead. I had to test out the trapdoor beneath the stage to make sure it was working.

Shakespeare himself is appearing in the play as a ghost, and he needs to come up through the door and make it look as if he's appeared from nowhere.

Lawrence accidentally opened the trapdoor onto my head and almost knocked me out on three separate occasions. He gave me a five-minute break before making me try again after each one, which I'm sure he felt was very generous.

I hope he doesn't make the same mistake with Shakespeare himself. His head is precious, as it's where all the plays come from. And there isn't much hair protecting it, so he needs to be careful.

GET REAL

Shakespeare was an actor as well as a playwright. We don't know for sure which roles he played, but a book published a hundred years after his death claimed that he played the ghost of Hamlet's dead father.

Saturday 15th February

I was helping to carry some drums up to the gallery this morning when I got some terrible news. I would have to perform in *Hamlet* after all. Edward was meant to be playing a few of the smaller parts, but he's unwell and has had to go to the doctor to get rid of some blood, so Lawrence shared his roles among the company.

I was cast as Barnardo, one of the guards who sees the ghost. I was only in the first couple of scenes, and the scrap of paper with the part on was very small, but it was still my biggest role so far. Plus, I only had a couple of hours to learn it.

I felt myself panicking.

I hid at the back of theatre and tried to work out how I was going to deliver my lines. The play starts with me shouting 'Who's there?', then Francisco says, 'Nay, answer me: stand and unfold yourself'. Then I say 'Long live the king!'

This was only my second line, but I got completely stuck. I tried it a few ways, drawing out a different word each time, but they all sounded wrong.

LONG live the king·
Long *LIVE* the king·
Long live *THE* king·
Long live the *KING*·

I wish I hadn't written myself so many lines...

I went through my whole part, put my paper down, and tried to go through it from memory. The words wouldn't come.

I told myself not to worry. Anthony stands at the side of the stage with a copy of the play and hisses the lines if you forget them. But I hadn't seen anyone needing a 'prompt' so far, and I didn't want to be the first.

In the end, I remembered all my lines, but I don't think I acted much like a guard. I forgot to stand up straight, and I was so scared that my whole body was shaking.

It took all my concentration to remember the words, so I didn't think about how I was saying them. I didn't consider what sort of person Barnardo was or how he was feeling. In other words, I didn't act. I just spoke.

Oh well. It's not like I ever really wanted to be an actor. It's just that if I could be good at it, I could get paid for it. And then I wouldn't have to help Mother and Philip with their disgusting work, and I could move out of our smelly house and afford all the pies I want.

After my role was over I went up to the gallery to watch the rest of the play, but I found it hard to concentrate. It was too long, and very glum, with lots of people complaining and talking about death. It's a shame Shakespeare didn't have me around when he was writing it, as I could have thought of a few ways to brighten it up.

I skulked off home after it had finished. I didn't want to face Lawrence after my poor performance.

Sunday 16th February

Lawrence came out to greet me as I soon as I got to the theatre this morning. I thought he was going to lecture me about not staying around to help Anthony clear up last night, but he threw his arms in the air and said my performance had been magnificent.

He said it was a brilliant choice to make
Barnardo terrified of the ghost. He said that
from my pale face and quaking hands you could
really believe I'd seen one.

He was so impressed he even gave me a penny
to buy myself a mincemeat pie. I thought about
telling him that I hadn't really been acting
at all and I was genuinely frightened, but I
wanted the pie, so I kept quiet.

Philip was really jealous when I told him about
the pie this evening. They've been eating a
pottage made from the leftovers of the pig's
head for the last few nights, and he got angry
with me for not bringing some pie home for
him. I told him it served him right for refusing
to share the pig's ears.

GET REAL

Pottage was a thick stew made by boiling ingredients like oats, cabbages, radishes, pumpkins, peas, beans and lentils with any meat or fish that could be found. It would sometimes be left in a cauldron over a fire for days, with extra ingredients added over time.

Monday 17th February

Shakespeare was backstage while I was cleaning up this morning, and he asked me what I thought of *Hamlet*.

He kept on saying that he wanted my honest opinion, so I gave it. I said it was too long and gloomy.

Shakespeare got really offended and said the play was meant to be dark and life wasn't all jokes and fun. He didn't exactly need to tell me that when I'd just spent an hour picking nutshells out of the ground.

He shouldn't ask people what they really think if he's going to be so sensitive. Also, the whole crowd seemed to love the play, so why worry if one person didn't think it was that great?

Anyway, we're doing it again next week, and I've promised to watch it again. Maybe it's better the second time.

Tuesday 18th February

We did *Love Labour's Won* this afternoon, and I played an assistant to the princess. Luckily, all my lines were over by the end of the first act, so I managed to sneak up to the gallery and watch the rest. I thought it was brilliant, one of the best plays Shakespeare has ever written. The crowd loved it too, and you could hardly hear what the actors were saying above the laughter.

I made sure to tell Shakespeare how much I liked it afterwards, and I hope it made up for giving my honest view about *Hamlet*. I've started calling him 'the Bard' now, which means 'poet'. I thought it would be a fun nickname. But he finds it really annoying and wants me to stop.

I don't know what he's worried about. It will never catch on.

GET REAL

Love's Labour's Won *is one of Shakespeare's lost plays. It's mentioned in a list of his works published in the sixteenth century, but no copies have survived. Some people think the play was a sequel to* Love's Labour's Lost, *while others think it was just an alternative title to an existing play. We'll never know, unless someone finds a dusty old copy and solves the mystery.*

Shakespeare's other famous lost play is called Cardenio, *and is thought to have been written with another playwright called John Fletcher.*

Wednesday 19th February

I was telling Philip about Shakespeare tonight
when he complained that I always tell him
about my day, but never ask how his was.

That's because his day involved nothing more
than dipping leather into salt, lime and wee
and washing it with poo. And I didn't need him
to tell me that because I could smell it as soon
as he walked in.

But just to make it fair I had to listen to him describing some great dog poo he found under some horse poo today. It was quite useful because I was feeling quite hungry until I heard his story, so at least it stopped me thinking about food.

Thursday 20ᵗʰ February

We did *Hamlet* again today. Shakespeare was so distracted by his writing that he forgot to take his place under the trapdoor and we started late. As the first person to speak, I was the one who got pelted with nutshells.

I went back up to the gallery afterwards and gave the play another go. I liked it better this time, though I still prefer stuff like *Love's Labour's Won* and *A Midsummer Night's Dream*.

I was especially impressed with Nicholas's performance as Hamlet, and I tried to work out what he was doing to make the words sound so good. He really makes you think he's the character rather than an actor. At times I forgot I was in a theatre at all, and felt like I was listening in to someone's private thoughts.

When I was clearing up the tiring house afterwards, I picked up the huge wad of paper with Hamlet's lines on. I looked around to check I was alone, cleared my throat and read some out loud:

To be, or not to be: that is the question:
Whether 'tis nobler in the mind to suffer
The slings and arrows of outrageous fortune,
Or to take arms against a sea of troubles,
And by opposing end them?

I could tell I wasn't delivering the words as well as Nicholas, and I had no idea how to do it better. I sounded so flat and boring. I wondered if acting was just something you could or couldn't do, and I didn't have the talent for it.

I stared at the lines and thought about what they really meant. It's a typically glum moment from this depressing play, when Hamlet is wondering whether it's better to be alive or dead. He doesn't enjoy life, but he worries that being dead could be even worse. I tried to make myself feel as sad as Hamlet is when he says the lines.

I eventually managed it by thinking about all the times Lawrence sent me out to get a pie for Shakespeare without getting one for myself. Then I tried the speech again. When I finished, I heard someone clapping behind me.

I turned and saw Lawrence. He grinned and said he could tell I was hungry to play Hamlet, but I wouldn't be getting star roles anytime soon. Then he told me about how he'd spent years in small parts before getting a lead, while massaging his forehead as if the memory was causing him actual pain.

He hurried away before I could explain that I didn't want to play Hamlet or any other massive part. I'm happy to keep doing the same small roles forever, and the only thing I'm hungry for is more pies.

GET REAL

Hamlet *remains one of the most popular plays in the world, and the story has been adapted into many forms. One of the retellings you might have seen is Disney's film* The Lion King. *Like Hamlet, Simba is a prince whose uncle kills his father to take the throne. They both eventually battle their uncles to take revenge. Hamlet never gets to sing any songs with meerkats and warthogs, though, so it's not exactly the same.*

Friday 21st February

I saw Nicholas in the tiring house this morning, so I told him how much I'd enjoyed his performance as Hamlet. He told me I was wrong and he'd been pathetic, so I shrugged and got on with my work.

I thought that might be the end of the conversation, but Nicholas obviously wasn't done. He stared at me and cleared his throat.

I had to tell him over and over again how brilliant he'd been, so he could pretend to be modest and deny it. This went on for ages and I have decided not to bother complimenting him again.

This afternoon Lawrence announced that our next plays will be *The Comedy of Errors*, *The Merchant of Venice* and *Romeo and Juliet*. I'm playing attendants in all of them, so I won't have much to do.

Lawrence said he knew I'd be disappointed, but to stick with it because the big parts might come sooner than I think.

I hope they don't. The only parts I want are attendants, servants, messengers, soldiers and guards. I'll even be a tree if they need one. As long as I don't get any leads.

Saturday 22nd February

Forget *Hamlet*, THIS is a tragedy. Nicholas has left our company to join our rivals The Admiral's Men. Apparently, he didn't feel appreciated here. And that's right after I spent an entire morning telling him how brilliant he was.

He was meant to be playing Juliet in *Romeo and Juliet*, which meant Lawrence had to recast the role with just two days to go. And instead of giving it to one of the more experienced actors, he's putting ME in the role.

He worked himself up into tears of joy as he was telling me, no doubt thinking he was giving me the big break I craved. I was so frightened that no words came out when I tried to speak. He said I didn't know how to thank him and that was fine. I could thank him with a brilliant performance instead. Then he handed me the wad of paper with Juliet's lines on and hurried off.

So Lawrence wasn't lying when he said I'd be getting main roles sooner than I expected. I thought he was talking about years rather than hours.

I can't do this. There are hundreds of lines to learn, and I have to appear in all five acts. I'm bound to forget my lines and get pelted with dead dogs.

I'm going to quit. Lawrence can't force me to take this on. I'll tell him this has all been a terrible mistake and he should pick someone

who has some actual talent for acting, like
Spud. Then I'll apologise to Mother and go
hunting for dog poo with her and Philip and I'll
never go near a theatre ever again.

Sunday 23rd February

I tried my best to get out of the role, but
Lawrence wouldn't let me. He said that
everyone gets nervous the first time they
step up to the big time.

I kept trying to tell him that I was a terrible
actor, but he just told me I was great and the
crowd would love me. He must have thought
I was fishing for compliments like Edward or
Nicholas, but I was being serious.

I can't act, and even if I could, the crowd would
never accept me as a replacement for Nicholas.
He had loads of fans. As soon as I open my

mouth they'll realise I'm not as good as him and march away to watch The Admiral's Men instead.

And then Lawrence will have to sell the Globe to become another bear-baiting pit and more bears will die and it will all be because of me.

GET REAL

Some Elizabethan actors became huge stars that could draw big crowds. The most popular one in Shakespeare's era was Richard Burbage, who was the first to play roles such as Hamlet and Richard III.

Monday 24th February

I stumbled into the Globe this morning,
clutching my wad of paper. I hadn't slept at
all, but I'd at least managed to go through the
whole play. I needed someone to test me on my
lines, but there was no one around.

Anthony was in the tiring house, but he was too
busy sorting costumes. Shakespeare turned up
next, and I thought he might be able to help,
but he'd just had a great idea for a scene in
King Lear, and he wanted to get it down before
he forgot it. Lawrence turned up next, but he
had plenty to do before the performance too.

I could do nothing but pace up and down on the
empty stage and mutter my lines.

I wondered how I'd manage to deliver them
properly even if I did remember them. How
could I make thousands of strangers believe I

was a rich young Italian girl in a doomed love affair? I've never even met an Italian, never mind a rich young doomed one.

Soon Anthony dragged me into the tiring house for my costume fitting. The metal corset dug into

my ribs and the frame for the dress was so wide I wondered if I'd even get out onto the stage.

Lawrence clapped his hands together when he saw me and said I'd be fabulous. I tried one last time to tell him I couldn't do it, but he rushed away without listening.

Anthony fixed my wig on, and it was soon time for him to run up the ladder and sound the trumpet.

I waddled out awkwardly in my huge dress. My first few lines weren't too tricky. They were mostly short answers to questions. The real test started in the fifth scene, where Romeo and Juliet meet and have their first kiss. I began my first line, 'Good pilgrim, you do wrong your hand too much'. I pictured the words on my piece of paper and said them out loud. Then the imaginary piece of paper went away. My mind was blank.

I tried to make the words come back. They wouldn't.

I glanced around the crowd with no idea what to do. A man with red hair was cracking open some nuts and tossing them into his open mouth. I wondered how long it would be before he started throwing them at me.

I spotted Spud at the front of the pit, grinning. Seeing a familiar face somehow made it worse. It made me realise that it was really happening. I'd forgotten my lines in front of three thousand people.

Something came back into my mind. Not a line, but an instruction. If I forgot what to say, I needed to look at the door to the tiring house, where Anthony would be waiting to prompt me.

I turned the door. Anthony wasn't there.

The one time I needed him, he'd gone off to faff around with his costumes.

My heart was racing and my throat was dry. There was nothing else for it. I was going to have to apologise to the crowd. I hadn't remembered my lines, I wasn't cut out to be an actor and I was going to spend the rest of my life with my hands stinking of salt, lime and wee.

I tried to say all of this, but what came out of my mouth was 'which mannerly devotion shows in this'. It was my next line. It had somehow bypassed my mind and come straight out of my mouth.

I continued with the scene, and managed to get to the end of it. I felt a stab of embarrassment when it was time to do the kiss. Spud was watching, and he was bound to tease me about it afterwards. At least Philip wasn't in the audience too. He'd have been making kissing noises and giggling from his side of the room for the next year if he'd seen it.

I went blank three more times, and the same thing happened. My mind raced with thoughts that I was ruining the play for everyone, I looked around for Anthony and found he wasn't there, felt like giving up, and then the right words came out of my mouth.

So I managed to remember my words, except for the few awkward pauses. But I could tell my performance wasn't good. I'd forgotten I was even meant to be Juliet. I was just me, rushing out the words and trying to get over my fear of being on stage.

By the end of the play, I couldn't hide my disappointment any more. I blurted out my final lines through tears.

The whole thing had been a disaster.

I didn't want to see anyone afterwards. I went straight home and got into bed. Philip soon came up and told me about his day treating the leather. I thought I'd better listen, because I'll need to know about it soon.

There's no way Lawrence will keep me on after that performance.

Chapter 4

Rising star

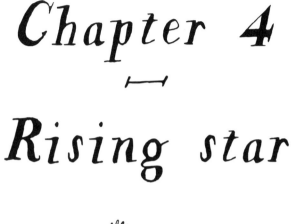

Tuesday 25th February

I couldn't bring myself to go to the Globe this morning. I knew I'd been terrible as Juliet and I didn't want to find out how disappointed everyone was.

Instead I wandered through the streets and ended up at the river. I gazed at the boats bobbing up and down on the clear water. There were the small dung boats dumping rubbish from the streets into the middle of the river. There were the wherries bringing passengers over from the north bank. And there were the huge ships unloading cargo in distant wharves.

Towering over everything was London Bridge. It's lined with shops and houses, so it feels like you're on a street when you're crossing it, but it looks amazing from down on the bank. A row of huge stone pillars support giant timber buildings that rise up to four storeys high.

I was wondering how long I could get away with pretending to Mother and Father that I was still going to the Globe, and just go down to the river every day, when someone tapped me on the shoulder.

I turned around and saw Spud. I was expecting him to tease me about the kissing scene, but instead he said he'd really liked the play, and that I'd been good in it.

I asked him what it had looked like when I forgot my lines, but he said he hadn't noticed. Maybe what seemed like minutes of awkward silence to me were really just a few seconds?

I couldn't work out if Spud was just being nice so I'd keep trying to get him a role, so I went to the Globe to see what everyone there thought.

Lawrence rushed over to meet me. Instead of telling me off, he said I'd been fabulous. He leapt around the stage, reproducing my performance. He said I'd given a brilliant portrayal of lovesickness with my pale skin, trembling hands and constant glances to the side, as if I was overwhelmed with emotion.

I didn't get a chance to explain I was really just looking for a prompt.

Lawrence said that my breakdown into tears at the end proved I had raw natural talent, and there would be more big roles on the way. He said he'd hire another apprentice to do the small jobs, so I could concentrate on my roles.

Then he gave me a penny to go out and buy a pie. I wanted to tell him that I didn't enjoy it and I don't want any more lead roles, but I decided to wait until after the pie.

By the time I got back, I'd thought better of saying anything. I need to think about what happened first.

Wednesday 26th February

Looking back on my performances, I think they've all gone well by accident. I was terrified of being on stage, which made it look like I was terrified of a ghost. I was sick with worry about forgetting my lines, which suited the role of a lovesick girl. Even my impatient shouting over the noise of the crowd worked well for the angry Hostess in *The Taming of the Shrew*.

So my acting career has all been based on mistakes. But maybe I could play the roles well on purpose from now on. Next time Lawrence gives me a part, I'll learn the lines, then I'll think about what sort of person the character is meant to be and how they'd say them.

Thursday 27th February

Okay, I have a bit more notice this time. I have another big role coming up, but not for a week. I'll be playing Beatrice in *Much Ado about Nothing*. It's a really good role because she spends most of her time insulting another character called Benedick, so I could get plenty of laughs. She's a very confident character, so this time it won't suit the play if I'm nervous. I'll have to be loud and clear on stage.

Friday 28th February

This morning I told Father that my first big role went well and I have another one coming up. He didn't seem very impressed at first, but then he put down the shoe he was working on and asked how many people came to these plays. I told him we regularly get three thousand. He stopped for a moment and scratched his chin. Then he came up with a really terrible idea.

Father wants me to interrupt one of my roles
to tell the audience how brilliant his shoes are.
He said that if just ten people from the massive
crowd paid attention and bought some, he could
afford some more pigs' heads for the pottage.

As if I'd be allowed to stay in the company
after trying something like that. Next time I'm

Juliet, I'm hardly going to break away from expressing my sorrow and heartache to mention that at least I have comfortable shoes which were very reasonably priced. Even if Lawrence didn't kill me, Shakespeare would.

Saturday 1st March

Before I play Beatrice, I've got a small role in *Julius Caesar*. I'll be a man called Voluminous who refuses to hold his sword out for his friend Brutus to impale himself on. I only have three lines, but unfortunately they're right at the end, so I can't get my role out of the way and watch the rest.

Anthony is getting flustered because there are a lot of props and costumes to sort out. The play is set in Italy hundreds of years ago, where they used to wear massive pieces of cloth called togas. They seem like a weird thing to wear, but who knows? Maybe one day people will look back on modern clothes like doublets, farthingales and ruffs, and think they're strange too.

GET REAL

The Elizabethans wore many fashions that look odd to us now. Doublets were short, tight jackets, typically worn with baggy knee-length trousers, and ruffs were lace collars that were often very elaborate.

Sunday 2nd March

The crowd really enjoyed *Julius Caesar*, and I quite liked what I managed to glimpse from inside the tiring house. Julius Caesar himself died quite early on, which I found surprising, given that the play is named after him.

Edward, who was playing Julius Caesar, had to hide a bladder full of pig's blood under his toga so it looked like he was bleeding everywhere when he got stabbed. Anthony seemed very pale as he gazed at this from the stage door and I wondered if it was too violent for him. Then I remembered he'd be the one washing the costumes afterwards. A minute of gory fun for the audience meant an hour of toga-scrubbing for him when the play was done.

Shakespeare was there, but instead of sitting at his desk, he was pacing up and down with his hands behind his back. He said he'd finished *King Lear*, and was trying to think of a new idea.

I told him to do a sequel to *Julius Caesar*, seeing as though the crowd like it so much. Caesar's ghost turns up briefly in Act IV, but he could appear throughout the sequel, doing hilarious things like turning people into donkeys and making them drink love potions.

Shakespeare didn't think much of my idea, but that's only because he didn't come up with it himself. You can bet he'd be writing *The Merry Ghost of Julius Caesar* right now if he'd thought of it.

Monday 3rd March

We did another Roman play today, which was called *Titus Andronicus*. I didn't have a part in it, but I had to help out with all the special effects. This meant going round to all the butchers' stalls and buying their spare blood, bladders and innards, then lugging the disgusting stuff back and helping Anthony sort it out. I think the butchers must have given me some rotten stuff they wanted to shift, because it really ponged.

When it was all done, Lawrence said I could go and watch the play, and he gave me a penny to buy a pie. I bought one and took it up to the gallery, though I didn't feel very hungry after handling all that horrible stuff.

The play turned out to be so gory that I couldn't eat the pie anyway. Even though I knew it

This smells offal!

was all just special effects, I got caught up in the story and I couldn't stop myself thinking it was real.

I was just getting my appetite back by the end of the play and was about to tuck into my snack, when Titus revealed he'd tricked Tamora into eating her own sons by baking them in a pie. I gave up trying to eat mine and tossed it to the ground.

The crowd loved every revolting moment, and hissed and booed at all the villains, which was pretty much everyone as far as I could tell. But I found it all a bit too horrible. If I want to make myself feel queasy, I'll go to London Bridge and stare at the severed heads of traitors. The theatre is meant to be fun.

The actors were slipping over in the intestines by the end. I went home as soon as it was over, as I knew Anthony would ask me to help clean the mess if he spotted me. He's probably still washing the blood off the stage as I write this.

GET REAL

Titus Andronicus *was Shakespeare's first tragedy, and it's easily his most violent. It was a huge hit with Elizabethan audiences, but fell out of favour in the 18th and 19th centuries. However, the play has become popular again in recent years, as gory stories have come back into fashion.*

Tuesday 4th March

I was struggling to remember my lines for *Much Ado About Nothing*, so I asked Father if he could help by doing Benedick's part. I offered to tell him what the lines were because he can't read, which got things off to a bad start. He hates it when I mention that.

We soon got into a massive row, with me saying he should support my ambition, and him saying I should learn a useful skill instead.

I said I'd get pelted by rotten food if I got my lines wrong. This gave Father the ridiculous idea of handing out shoes to angry members of the audience, so I could comment on how strong and reasonably priced they were as they hit me.

Then I realised something. I could use my anger with Father to become Beatrice. Instead of arguing about his terrible plan, I started yelling my lines at him, and as I heard them coming from my mouth I knew they sounded better.

He said I wasn't making any sense, and hanging around with theatre types had made me soft in the head, but I didn't care. For the first time, I was in control of how I was delivering my lines. I was finally acting.

Wednesday 5ᵗʰ March

When I got to the tiring house this morning
I found that Shakespeare was already there,
scribbling away on a big block of paper. I
asked him what he was writing, and he said
he'd had the brilliant idea of doing a sequel to
Julius Caesar.

I can't believe it. That was my idea. He's
decided to write about what happened when
the Roman general Mark Anthony went to
Egypt and fell in love with Queen Cleopatra,
which he's read about in a history book. So it's
not quite the same as my story about Caesar's
ghost, but it would be nice to get some sort
of credit.

Shakespeare said I could play Cleopatra when
he'd finished it, but I said I'd rather be given
half his fee.

GET REAL

Shakespeare didn't always write plays on his own. He is known to have collaborated on some works, such as The Two Noble Kinsmen, *which was written with John Fletcher. Some researchers study patterns of word use to work out exactly who wrote which lines.*

He usually drew his stories from things like historical accounts, rather than inventing them himself. For example, both Julius Caesar *and* Anthony and Cleopatra *were inspired by* Parallel Lives, *a series of biographies of ancient Greeks and Romans written by Plutarch.*

Thursday 6ᵗʰ March

I remembered all my lines as Beatrice tonight, and I think I delivered them well. I didn't feel like I was forceful enough at first, but then I remembered my argument with Father and it helped me become angrier.

Afterwards, Lawrence clasped my shoulder and said I'd been magnificent, and for once it didn't come as a huge surprise.

Next week I'll be playing the part of Titania in *A Midsummer Night's Dream*. Edward is going to play Bottom again, so my biggest challenge will be keeping a straight face when I'm on stage with him.

Friday 7th March

I think I've learned my lines as Titania now,
and I've got a good idea how I want to deliver
them. I've been keeping Philip awake by
practising them at night. With three days to go
until my next big role, I'm actually feeling quite
relaxed about it.

Saturday 8th March

Okay, so now I'm not relaxed. It turns out that
Lawrence forgot to tell me something rather
important about the upcoming production of
A Midsummer Night's Dream. We won't be
performing it for the regular Globe crowd. We'll
be performing it for the queen.

That's right. I've got to be a convincing queen of
fairies in front of the actual queen. If I get my
lines wrong, she'll probably chop off my head
and stick it on London Bridge.

And it won't just be Queen Elizabeth watching. There will be a whole crowd of important noblemen and officials gathered in the great hall of Greenwich Palace.

Just a few weeks ago, I was terrified of saying a few lines in front of some apple-munching groundlings. Now I have to play a major role in front of the richest people in the country. I'll be surprised if I can speak at all.

GET REAL

Queen Elizabeth I liked to watch plays, but she didn't need to venture out to theatres like the Globe. The best acting companies would travel out to her palaces and perform. A stage would be built at one end of a hall and a passageway would be curtained off to create a backstage area.

Chapter 5

A royal performance

Sniff... I'm so proud!

Sunday 9th March

I'm still nervous about performing for the queen, but at least it's got me some respect from Mother.

As soon as I got home tonight, Mother started yelling at me for staying out late with my acting friends when I could have been helping her and Philip out. But when I told her I'd be performing for the queen, she stopped in the middle of her rant. In a quiet voice, she said I'd done well and she was very pleased.

She looked around in panic, as if saying something nice for once might make her brain explode. She fixed her small dark eyes on Father, scowled and told him off for making shoes too slowly.

We all breathed a sigh of relief that the awkward moment was over and things were back to normal.

Unfortunately, Father came up with another of his silly ideas to promote his shoes, so I had to go up to my room to avoid arguing with him. This time he wanted me to write a song about how great his shoes are, and sing it to the queen in a break between scenes. I told him I'd think about it, even though there's more chance of me jumping in a bear-baiting pit.

Monday 10th March

I told Spud I'd be performing for the queen and he was also very impressed. He said Lawrence must think I'm a truly brilliant actor if he's asked me to perform for a royal, and he hopes to do it himself one day.

He also told me to be careful not to cast a glance at the queen, because apparently she's one of the most beautiful women in the world, and it could be distracting. His advice has made me even more nervous. What if she's so beautiful that I dry up and bring the whole play to a halt?

Tuesday 11th March

Tomorrow is the big day. We're travelling to Greenwich by boat, as going by river is always the best way to get anywhere, especially if you're carrying costumes and props. We have to wait until the afternoon when the tides are going out, and it's much cheaper. Each boat costs eight pennies if you're travelling with the tide, but twelve pennies if the tide is against you. Edward wanted to get there sooner so he could focus on getting into character, but Lawrence insisted on making the savings.

Wednesday 12th March

We got into the boats this afternoon. Lawrence went in the one at the front, along with most of the costumes. I clambered into the one at the back, and tried to make myself comfortable on a pile of prop flowers and lanterns.

I was feeling fine at first, but when we approached London Bridge I saw the heads on spikes and it made me worry that I'd mess up and end up on one. Then we passed the Tower, and I spotted Traitor's Gate, where the boats containing people accused of treason go in. I wondered if the queen would send me through there to a lifetime of imprisonment if I got my lines wrong. I decided to spend the rest of the journey with my eyes on my stack of paper, going over my part again.

When I looked up I saw we were already in Greenwich and the royal palace was on our right. A man with a beard and a velvet cloak led us across a wide courtyard and into the passageway that was to be our temporary tiring house. We had to sort out all our props and costumes in the narrow space, and Anthony got very flustered.

Edward demanded to be given space to walk up and down and get into character, and he kept bumping into Anthony while he was trying to put costumes on.

Anthony shouted at Edward to keep back when he was fixing my corset and farthingale, and Edward yelled back at him that actors were more important than costumes and he should know his place.

The play soon started, and the petty squabbles cut out. I couldn't sneak forward and peep through the curtain in my bulky costume, so I had to stay back and wait for my entrance in Act II. It seemed to be going pretty well, though unsurprisingly the audience were quieter than the Globe crowd. I wondered if they'd throw roast swans rather than dead dogs if they didn't like it.

It was finally time to step out. The great hall had a high ceiling and large windows that threw long strips of sunlight across the floor. At the far end were rows of seats filled with smartly dressed people.

The queen herself was right in the middle on a fancy wooden chair with a high canopy made from red velvet.

I forced myself to ignore these grand surroundings and focus on my role. I told myself I was Titania and not Robert, and that I was in an enchanted forest and not in Greenwich.

The audience seemed to be laughing in the right places. As soon as the queen herself giggled, the others would guffaw and mutter things like 'very good'. I wondered if most of them were watching her more than me.

It was all going well until I glanced over at the queen. I'd promised myself I wouldn't, in case I got distracted by her beauty, but curiosity got the better of me.

The queen was sitting forward on her chair with her arms resting in her lap. She had a red wig, a long nose, cracked pale skin and rotten black teeth in swollen gums. I couldn't take my eyes off her. She was the most horrible-looking person I'd ever seen.

I stopped in the middle of a line with my mind totally blank. I tried to speak, but could do nothing but stare at the weird-looking monarch.

Anthony stuck his head out from behind the curtain and hissed the next part of my line. His eyes were wide and his skin had gone pale.

This snapped me right back into it and I got
on with the play. The queen kept on laughing,
which meant the noblemen around her did too,
and it looked like I'd got away with it.

After we'd finished, the queen declared that
she'd been greatly amused, and everyone let out
a huge cheer.

We were led to a banqueting hall and treated
to a huge feast. Even before anything had been
served, I was astonished by the clean linen
tablecloths, folded napkins and silver knives
and spoons. Then the queen's staff brought out
an incredible selection of meat on wide dishes.
There was beef, veal, mutton, lamb, pork, goose
and rabbit. And they were topped with sauces
made from expensive flavourings like sugar,
salt, cinnamon, vinegar and mustard.

They even served a strange plant that comes from the New World and looks like it should be poisonous. I found it was a bit tough without much flavour but it didn't taste too bad.

I asked the man next to me what it was and he said a word that sounded like 'pot-A-toe'. I don't think these potato things will take off with a funny name like that. I thought they looked a bit like Spud, so I decided to call them spuds instead. I think that suits them much better.

After a while, a hush fell across the room and everyone got to their feet. The queen was making her way round to congratulate us all, flanked by officials.

I bowed as she approached. To my surprise, she stopped in front of me.

She glared at me and asked if I'd had a spot of trouble with my lines. The breath wafting out from between her black teeth was disgusting, and I was worried I'd bring up all that rich food. I'm pretty sure spewing on the queen is bad manners.

If I told the truth that her bizarre appearance had thrown me, my head would be on London Bridge before I could finish my sentence. I had to think fast.

I told the queen that I'd been distracted by her beauty. I said I'd heard talk of it, but nothing could have prepared me for the truth.

She nodded, and her officials muttered in agreement.

She continued along and I breathed a sigh of relief. Claiming the queen was attractive might be the most important lie I've ever told, as well as the biggest.

Thursday 13th March

On my way to the Globe I spotted Spud and told him all about yesterday. He asked if Queen Elizabeth was really as beautiful as everyone said, and when I told him she actually looked like something that would turn up in your dreams if you ate too much cheese, he told me to be quiet in case any of her spies overheard and we got imprisoned in the Tower.

Now I understand what you need to be beautiful. You don't need eyes as bright as the sun, lips as red as coral or breath as sweet as perfume. You just need to imprison anyone who says you aren't.

When I got to the Globe, I asked Lawrence about why the queen looks so weird. In a loud voice, he said he had no idea what I was talking about, and he wouldn't hear a word against our glorious queen. Then he stuck his hand in front of his mouth and whispered his real answer.

Apparently, rich women like the queen use special powders to make themselves look paler, but over time this damages their skin and makes their hair fall out. They can also afford really sugary food, which rots their teeth.

If that's what luxury does to you, I'm glad I have no money.

120

GET REAL

Wealthy women like Queen Elizabeth I used a type of make-up made from a mixture of vinegar and white lead, causing horrific damage to their skin.

They enjoyed sweet treats that were full of sugar, such as gingerbread and marchpane, the forerunner of marzipan. Sugar was still very rare in England, as it had only recently started to be imported from the Caribbean.

Friday 14ᵗʰ March

I thought Lawrence would still be in a good mood this morning after our performance. But when I arrived at the Globe he was wailing and mopping his brow with the back of his hand.

121

He heard two boys talking outside his window as he woke up, and they were describing how brilliantly The Admiral's Men had performed Ben Jonson's play *Every Man in his Humour* for the queen the night after we did *A Midsummer Night's Dream*.

Apparently she laughed so much the play had to be halted three times, and she personally congratulated every member of the company twice afterwards. I hope they held their breath.

I remembered that Shakespeare had also heard two boys talking about how brilliant Ben Jonson and the Admiral's Men were outside his window. I said they were probably sending their young actors out to undermine us with fake conversations.

Lawrence said it sounded like the sort of sneaky thing the Admiral's Men would do.

122

But he still couldn't stop fretting. The queen wants a whole series of performances next month, and he's worried that The Admiral's Men will be asked to do them all.

Saturday 15th March

It turns out that Lawrence had nothing to worry about. I have plenty to worry about, however.

It seems the queen liked our performance so much she's invited us back to perform six more plays over six nights. I told Lawrence this was great news, but in truth I wasn't so sure.

It means I have to remember six different parts and perform them one after the other. This time I can't afford any mistakes. I've already pretended to be distracted by the queen's beauty, so I can't use that excuse again.

I'm playing Juliet and Titania again, so it shouldn't be too hard to get those roles back in my mind. But I've also got to play Luciana in *The Comedy of Errors*, Silvia in *The Two Gentlemen of Verona*, Mistress Ford in *The Merry Wives of Windsor* and Rosalind in *As You Like It*.

Sunday 16th March

This is all going wrong. I'm trying to learn every role at once and getting them mixed up. I'll be reciting a speech by Rosalind, then I'll switch to Mistress Ford, then I'll throw in a bit of Silvia before turning into Luciana. None of it is sticking in my mind properly.

And it isn't helping that Father keeps bursting into my room to ask if I can get my friend Shakespeare to write a book of poems about his

shoes to attract more customers. I said I was
sure the topic of sturdy footwear would be just
as inspiring as the classic themes of love, power
and revenge. He nodded, and I don't think he
even realised I was joking.

Monday 17th March

Everyone seemed very gloomy when I got to the
Globe this morning. Lawrence was slouching
on the edge of the stage and shaking his head,
while Edward was standing at the back and
gazing at a prop skull. I wondered if the stress
of learning so many parts was getting to
everyone else too. I asked Lawrence what the
matter was, and he said the queen had fallen ill
and our entire series of plays was cancelled.

I felt like celebrating, but I remembered I
should be sad about the queen, so I pretended

to cry. I must have acted well, because Lawrence grasped my hand and told me it would be fine, our good queen would pull through.

I hope she does, but not so quickly that we have to do all six performances. I think I'd have fallen ill too if I'd had to do them all.

Lawrence gave me a penny to buy a pie, but I was too tired to eat so I came back to bed. Lines from my roles are still swirling around my head, even though I don't need to know them now.

Saturday 22nd March

We're going to do *The Merry Wives of Windsor* at the Globe instead of the palace now. It means I can put my other scripts aside and focus on learning the part of Mistress Ford.

Lawrence mentioned he wanted some extras to play the children who pinch Falstaff while pretending to be fairies. I ran to get Spud right away.

Spud rushed back with me, and was so desperate for the part he even practised pinching as we ran, which was quite painful. But by the time we returned, Lawrence had already found some children from the street who wanted to do it.

I asked if he could try Spud out for one of the other roles while he was here, but he said he didn't look girlish enough for female roles.

It's a shame because Spud is a good actor, and Lawrence should give him a chance in one of the male roles if he isn't right for the women.

Spud thanked me for trying and trudged away
with his shoulders slumped.

Monday 24th March

Today was a horrible day, easily the worst since
I joined The Lord Chamberlain's Men.

The Merry Wives of Windsor went well at first,
with plenty of laughter from the pit. Edward,
who was playing Falstaff, got huge cheers for
every line because everyone loves the character
so much.

I was getting some good laughs as Mistress
Ford too. But they started to die out during Act
III. I was playing a scene with Mistress Page,
when a low murmur spread through the crowd.

Some of them began to weep and I heard a
woman wailing. I hadn't got a reaction like

this since the end of *Romeo and Juliet* and I wondered if I'd totally misunderstood the play. I'd thought it was a fun comedy, but maybe there was some tragic undertone I'd totally missed.

Then Lawrence pushed past us to address the crowd. He said we would abandon the performance as the queen had died.

I stood on the stage and watched the shocked crowd file out. Then I changed out of my costume and wandered back through the empty streets. When I got home, I went straight to bed. I was thinking of going over my lines by the light of my candle, but then I realised that the Globe would be closed while the country mourned the queen.

Elizabeth was on the throne for over forty years, so I've never known what it's like for a king or queen to die. So far it just feels empty.

GET REAL

Queen Elizabeth I died on 24th March 1603. The exact cause of her death isn't known, but some people think she was poisoned by the lead in her make-up. Others think she might have had an infection, or an illness like pneumonia.

It was reported that the queen's coronation ring had to be sawn off shortly before her death. She hadn't removed it for so long that the skin on her finger had grown around it.

Chapter 6

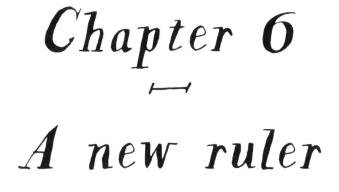

A new ruler

Tuesday 25th March

I wandered over to the Globe this morning to
see if I could help Lawrence with anything,
but he wasn't there. I found him in his house,
slumped back on a chair in his dining room
with his hands clasped to his forehead. There
was a pewter cup of ale and an untouched bowl
of pottage on the table in front of him.

Instead of greeting me, he recited the speech from *Hamlet* that begins, 'I have of late – but wherefore I know not – lost all my mirth'.

I asked him if he was grieving for the queen, but he said he was actually worrying about the company. He said he had no idea who would take over and whether they would like plays or not. They might want to ban them altogether. Or worse, the whole country could descend into a civil war and his precious theatre could be destroyed by a lawless mob.

He let out a sigh, then drank his ale in a few large gulps.

I told Lawrence it would all work out fine, but in truth I have no idea what's going to happen. Next time I write in here, I could be lying in a muddy ditch and trying to hide from angry rioters.

GET REAL

Water was considered unsafe to drink by most Elizabethans, and drinking ale or beer was more common.

Beer was made from barley, water and hops and kept for a long time, while ale was made without hops and had to be drunk within a few days.

Wednesday 26th March

It looks like the country won't collapse into chaos after all. King James of Scotland is going to take over. Apparently it's been the secret plan all along.

He used to be called James VI because Scotland has had five other kings called James, but we've never had one before, so now he's going to be called James I, which must be quite confusing for him.

No one knows that much about him, but everyone seems happy there is some sort of plan and that we aren't going to have a civil war or anything.

The new king is riding down from Scotland as I write this. I expect there are bigger things on his mind right now than plays, but I hope we can get some sort of indication of his views on theatres soon.

GET REAL

Queen Elizabeth I had no children, and it wasn't clear who would take over when she died. A number of different people thought they had a claim to the throne, and some believed this would lead to violence and unrest. But the change went smoothly in the end. Queen Elizabeth's advisors had been making secret plans for King James VI of Scotland to take over, which became known as 'the union of the crowns'.

Saturday 3rd May

Five days ago the late queen was buried in Westminster Abbey, and today our new king arrived in London. I went out to see him, because I thought I could ask him what he thought about plays, but it turned out to be impossible.

137

I managed to push through the crowds and cross London Bridge, but everywhere on the other side was as packed as the front of the pit at the Globe. There were people hanging out of windows, standing on stalls and balancing on roofs.

I tried making my way over to the Strand. This is the road that connects Westminster with the city. It's lined by grand houses, full of rich people and their servants. It's usually pretty empty, so I thought it would be a good place to get to see the king, but hundreds of other people had the same idea.

They all crowded in front of me as the king's carriage arrived, and I didn't even get to glimpse him, let alone discuss entertainment with him. We'll just have to wait longer to find out our fate.

Sunday 4th May

Once again, those sneaky Admiral's Men have sent young actors to wake Lawrence up by gossiping outside his window. And the news they brought this morning has really upset him.

The king is going to have a massive procession through the streets to mark his coronation, and his advisors have asked Ben Jonson from The Admiral's Men to write all the grand speeches.

Lawrence thinks the public will see it as official royal approval of The Admiral's Men, and that they'll overtake us to become the most popular playing company in London.

I told him to look on the bright side. A few days ago, we were worried that whoever took over might close the theatres. Now the king has asked a playwright to help with his coronation.

It might not be our playwright, but it's still a good sign.

GET REAL

Important events such as the crowning of a new monarch were marked by pageants, which were noisy and colourful processions through the streets. They often featured speeches written by famous playwrights such as Ben Jonson and Thomas Middleton.

Monday 5th May

Lawrence went to Shakespeare's house yesterday and asked if he would come up with some ideas for pageants, so he could send them to the Tower, where the king is staying.

Shakespeare said he hadn't been asked by the king, and he wasn't prepared to beg if he wanted Ben Jonson instead. I reckon he also thinks things like pageants are beneath him, and would rather spend his time writing new plays.

Now Lawrence is refusing to speak to him and I have to spend all my time carrying messages back and forth between them. He's also started referring to him as 'the Bard', because he knows how much that annoys him. Maybe my nickname will catch on after all.

If only the king could come to see one of our performances. Then he'd know that Shakespeare is better than Jonson, and that we're the best playing company.

GET REAL

King James I stayed at the Tower of London after he arrived in 1603. Back then, the Tower was home to a collection of wild animals, and James is thought to have enjoyed setting his dogs on the lions. This might seem very cruel, but getting animals to fight each other was very popular.

Saturday 24th May

I went out to see the pageant today, but it was too busy to see anything again. The streets were packed with a weird mix of wealthy men and women wearing thick woollen gowns over bright, clean clothes, and ordinary working people in dirty smocks and breeches.

I crossed London Bridge early this morning and walked for ages along the Strand until I found a free spot. I thought I might get a good view this time, but a group of rude people pushed in front of me just as it was about to begin.

I managed to glimpse some actors in fancy costumes of silk, velvet, satin and cloth of gold, as well as some drummers and trumpeters. I could hear Jonson's speeches bellowing out, but I couldn't make out the words over the din of music and cheering.

I know we get some noisy people in the pit at the Globe, but the crowd on the Strand were much louder. I can see why Shakespeare wouldn't want to spend ages writing something that's just going to be drowned out by drums and fireworks.

Tuesday 27th May

The pageant must have been a success because the king has asked Ben Jonson to write a masque for him. It will be like a sort of indoor pageant, with lots of fancy sets and costumes.

The Admiral's Men sent their young actors to gossip about it outside Lawrence's window again, which meant he started the day in the worst possible mood.

He demanded that Shakespeare write a masque for him to send to the king, and Shakespeare refused again, though he said he'd try and include a masque in a proper play, and he had an idea for one set on an island that might suit it.

This only made Lawrence angrier. He said he doesn't want another masterpiece from the Bard, he just wants something he can get to

the king fast to show we can do anything The Admiral's Men can. If they keep getting work from the new king, we might as well change our name to The Yesterday's Men.

GET REAL

Masques were a form of entertainment that combined singing, dancing and acting with lavish stage design. They were performed in honour of the queen or king. Ben Jonson wrote several masques featuring sets created by the architect Inigo Jones.

Shakespeare never wrote a full masque, though some of his plays feature them as interludes. The Tempest, *for example, features a scene in which Ariel summons spirits to perform one.*

Wednesday 4ᵗʰ June

Lawrence is sure he could convince the king we're the best playing company in a matter of minutes if he could only speak to him. But he has no idea how to get near him.

I said our whole company should just go down to the Tower, find the king and tell him how brilliant we are. We could even prove it by performing one of our plays.

Lawrence said we'd never get past the guards. They'd assume we were leading some sort of uprising, especially if we brought our prop daggers, and kill us on the spot.

He's probably right. But we've got to do something. We can't sit here sulking while the Admiral's Men become the king's favourites.

Thursday 5th June

I told Spud about our problems today, and he said it was a shame because he's seen The Admiral's Men perform and we're better.

I said I was sure the king would want us to perform if only he could hear some bits from Shakespeare's plays. Even a few lines would be enough to make him change his mind.

Then Spud had an idea. He said that the characters in Shakespeare's plays often disguise themselves as other people, so why couldn't we do the same? After all, there were hundreds of costumes in the Globe, and I could surely sneak a couple away.

He said that if a couple of Romans or fairies turned up at the Tower, the guards would be so confused they'd probably just let us in. Then we could go and make our case to the king.

148

At first I thought it was a silly idea. The guards would be as likely to stab us as let us in. But then I remembered the noblemen costumes Anthony has. I've seen a fancy jewel-encrusted doublet and ostrich feather hat I could wear, and a golden jacket Spud could wear.

No one would question we were true noblemen if we wore those. No ordinary people could afford any costumes like that. We'd look exactly like some of those important people who'd been sitting around the queen during *A Midsummer Night's Dream*.

But how would we know when to go to the Tower? We'd have to go when the king was expecting some genuine noblemen to arrive, or the guards would know we were lying, and imprison us on the spot.

Friday 13th June

The boys from the Admiral's Men woke Lawrence up again this morning with more gloating. They said the masque is taking place tomorrow night at the Palace of Whitehall and it's going to be the greatest spectacle ever seen.

I tried to cheer him up by saying that we'll always have the best plays and actors, even if The Admiral's Men have better sets and dancers. It was no use. He's convinced the new king will only like masques and our plays will be worthless now.

Then I realised something. If the masque is happening tomorrow night, it will be the perfect time to carry out Spud's plan. We won't need to get into the Tower now – we can just follow the hundreds of noblemen entering the palace.

We'll never get a better chance than this.

Chapter 7

A cunning plan

Saturday 14th June

We turned up at the Globe this afternoon
to find Anthony messing around with the
costumes. Even though we don't know when
we'll be able to put on plays again, he chose
today to come and sort through all his stuff.

I kept suggesting he should go home and rest,
but he said tidying would take his mind off
worrying about the new king.

In the end, I had to get Spud to
pretend there was a fire on the roof
to get Anthony out. This almost
didn't work, because he kept
running out, then popping back
to rescue more precious props
and costumes. Eventually
he got outside, carrying so
much stuff he collapsed into a
heap at the back door.

153

We grabbed the nobleman costumes and changed into them on our way to the river. Spud asked me lots of questions about the character he was playing, but I told him it would be better to keep quiet until we got in front of the king.

He seemed quite disappointed. I think he'd been looking forward to using his acting skills.

We found a boatman, but he wanted three pennies just to take us over to Whitehall. I suppose that's what you get for looking wealthy.

I managed to talk him down to a penny and we crossed over the river. We strode along the jetty, passed a huge chapel and wandered into a wide courtyard where men and women in expensive clothes were heading to an arched doorway.

We joined the back of a group and strolled right past the guards flanking the doorway.

We found ourselves inside a huge hall with a large square stage and rows of wooden chairs. Everyone else seemed to know where to sit, and for a few moments we dithered around and I worried someone would notice us. We ended up standing against the left wall, and nobody questioned us.

The king entered and took his place on a fancy chair with a large red canopy. The audience of dignified noblemen became an unruly rabble as he settled down, getting to their feet and barking compliments.

Everyone was so desperate to win the favour of the new king that it seemed impossible we'd ever get near him.

At least I could take a look at him. He had a white doublet with gold buttons and a frilly lace collar. He seemed quieter than the late queen, keeping his eyes on the ground and ignoring the racket of the mob.

The masque began, and though I hate to admit it, the performane was fantastic. A gallery above the stage was packed with musicians clutching viols, oboes and trumpets.

Below them ladies with pearls and feathers woven into their elaborate hairstyles leapt around in fine silk dresses. It was quite shocking to see actual women rather than boys dressed as them taking part in an entertainment. I hoped someone would be so outraged they'd call the whole thing to a stop, but the king looked happy, so nobody said a word.

The Admiral's Men followed them onstage, carrying shells, burning torches and huge wooden seahorses. Long stretches of blue cloth were billowed up and down to create an indoor ocean and for a moment I forgot I was in the palace and felt like I was on the deck of a sailing ship. Actors gave long speeches while music played and men and women danced in pairs, first skipping across the stage and then circling each other in nimble movements.

So much was going on it was a little overwhelming and I forgot why we'd gone there in the first place. The king could have been strolling around and asking if anyone wanted to have a chat for all I'd have known.

The whole thing must have cost an absolute fortune, and it was a shame they couldn't have put it on in a theatre so more people could have seen it. But the groundlings would probably just have thrown dead dogs and cats into the pretend sea anyway.

When the masque had finished, the king declared it the best entertainment he'd ever seen, and hoped it would be the first of many. This wasn't good news, and it snapped me out of my trance. I needed to speak to him before The Admiral's Men were appointed as his official players.

The king walked out into the courtyard and through a wide door into a banqueting hall, followed by the simpering herd of important people. The determined looks on their faces reminded me of Philip when he's chasing after dogs, except they were covered in fancy clothing rather than poo.

Inside, long wooden tables were set with silver plates and spoons, while servants set huge steaming dishes of carved mutton, venison, beef and swan.

I tried to speak to the king, but I still couldn't get close. He was walking around and congratulating the performers while the rich people flocked around him and tried to outdo each other with how much they could agree with him.

I gave up and wandered over to Spud, who had taken a seat and was tucking into some beef in pepper and vinegar. He said we'd be in trouble if we were caught anyway, so we might as well make the most of it.

I shrugged and joined him. The food was just as delicious as it had been at the other palace, but I was too frustrated to enjoy it. We'd got so close to the king, yet we were so far from actually being able to speak to him.

Spud pointed out Ben Jonson on a table on the other side of the hall. He had dark curly hair, deep-set black eyes and a permanent scowl, even though the masque seemed to have gone well. I guessed he was just like Shakespeare, who forgets the million compliments he receives so he can brood on one slight criticism.

I kept glancing over at the king. He looked tired, and was nodding whenever anyone spoke to him, but I doubted he was actually listening.

I looked down to grab some mutton, and when I looked back up the king had disappeared, leaving a gap in the middle of the crowd of noblemen. I leapt to my feet and pulled Spud after me.

A lone figure was stepping out into the dark courtyard.

It was the king. This was our chance.

We crept after him, keeping our distance as he strolled ahead. He planted his hands on his hips, looked up at the clear night sky and sighed.

I was trying to work out what to do when Spud ran up to him and put on a posh voice. He said we were very important guests and we wished to introduce ourselves. He couldn't resist the chance to show off his acting ability, even though I'd warned him against it.

It's not easy being king.

The king said we sounded like just the sort of people he'd come outside to get away from.

I shoved Spud aside and told the truth. I said we were from a company of actors and we wanted him to know that we were the best in London.

I was expecting him to get angry with us for tricking our way into the palace and chop our heads off. But instead he said he liked plays and asked us why I thought our company was so brilliant.

I was shocked, and didn't know what to say. I'd imagined that if I ever got this far, I'd be able to reel off a million reasons why Shakespeare was the greatest playwright and we were the best actors. But now the moment had arrived, I went as blank as that time I played Juliet. Spud jumped in front of me and recited some of the best Falstaff lines from the Henry plays.

The king didn't crack a smile, but at least it bought me some time. I decided to act out some of the best Benedick and Beatrice scenes from *Much Ado About Nothing*. This stuff had gone down so well at the Globe, I thought the king would collapse in hysterics. But he didn't even titter.

Spud tried acting out some stuff from *The Taming of the Shrew*. Still nothing.

The only thing I could think of was to try something from *A Midsummer Night's Dream*. That's the play that had made me a fan of the theatre in the first place, and if the king didn't laugh, it would mean he had terrible taste.

I took a deep breath, then acted out the scene where Titania falls in love with Bottom, jumping back and forth as I acted out both roles. In the Globe, we had to leave long gaps

for the laughter of the crowd to die down.
Now when I left pauses I could hear nothing
but the distant sound of conversation in the
banqueting hall.

I finished and stared at the king. He wasn't
even smirking.

He said we'd made a good effort, but the plays
didn't sound like his sort of thing. Then he
turned and wandered back to the hall.

I slumped down to the ground and Spud joined
me. It was all over. I'd had a chance and I'd
blown it. Other funny scenes from the plays
raced through my mind and I wondered if I
could have chosen better.

Ben Jonson and the Admiral's Men would now
be the king's favourites, everyone would flock to
their plays and we'd fall out of favour. With no

royal backing, the Puritans would probably come and burn down the Globe and no one would care.

We needed to get back and return the clothes, but I couldn't bring myself to stand up. I just stayed on the floor, feeling sorry for myself. Without realising I was doing it, I started reeling off a miserable speech from *Hamlet*, just as Lawrence had done when I visited him at home.

'I have of late – but wherefore I know not – lost all my mirth, forgone all custom of exercises, and indeed it goes so heavily with my disposition that this goodly frame, the earth, seems to me a sterile promontory...'

I got so lost in the words that I didn't hear the footsteps behind me. I had no idea someone was with us until I'd finished the speech and I heard clapping.

I turned around and saw it was the king. He said the speech had been much better than the other stuff and he wanted to hear more from the same play. I leapt up and told him all about *Hamlet*, then broke into the 'O that this too too solid flesh would melt' speech and then followed it with 'To be or not to be.'

The king said that Hamleg sounded like an excellent play, and he'd be happy to watch it if I brought my playing company to the hall, so he could see where the leg of ham fitted into it. I think my English accent might have confused him about the title, but I didn't want to correct him while I was on a roll.

I said we could do it any time the king wanted, and he chose next Wednesday.

The king said he looked forward to seeing my full performance and strolled back. I had a huge grin on my face for two minutes. Then I realised I'd just promised to learn all of the lines for the part of Hamlet in four days. I really know how to make things difficult for myself, don't I?

Sunday 15th June

I meant to wake up early this morning and take the costumes back, but I was so tired I slept until noon. By the time I got to the Globe, Anthony was frantically searching for the clothes, while Lawrence had convinced himself the boys from The Admiral's Men had stolen them and was lying on the stage and fanning himself with a wad of paper.

They both looked very confused when I turned up with the precious clothes in my arms.

I got Lawrence to sit down and I told him all that had happened yesterday. His reaction went from anger that we'd taken the clothes to joy that we'd convinced the king to watch Hamlet, to panic that we had so little time to get ready. He switched from clenching his fists to clapping to biting his fingernails in the space of about five minutes.

Lawrence said the king obviously prefers tragedy to comedy, and I should have acted out a greater variety of roles in the first place. It was quite ungrateful of him to complain after all I'd done for him, but I suppose he's right. Just because I prefer light-hearted plays, it doesn't mean everyone does.

It should suit Shakespeare, because most of his new ideas sound even gloomier than *Hamlet*.

Anthony dashed into the tiring house and emerged with the massive stack of paper that was Hamlet's part. I pretended that the king had also insisted Spud play Hamlet's friend Horatio, which wasn't true, but I thought I'd take the chance to finally get him a role.

Anthony fetched Horatio's part too and I took it round to Spud's house and gave him the good news. He wanted me to help him rehearse but I had to go back home. I've got to learn the longest part Shakespeare ever wrote in the next three days. I'd better get on with it.

Tuesday 17th June

Okay, I think the lines have sunk in now. Which gives me a day to work out how I'm going to perform them. But there are so many different ways I could say the words. I'd need a whole month to work it out properly.

I'll just have to hope the excitement pulls me through, because at the moment I have no idea what Hamlet is really meant to be like.

Wednesday 18th June

We carried our costumes and props down to the river and took boats to Whitehall this afternoon.

We then wandered across the jetty and into the courtyard, clasping our costumes, skulls, shovels, daggers and cups.

Two guards saw our group approaching and ran over to block the doorway. But then they went to check with the king's advisors, who confirmed that he was expecting a group of actors and we weren't trying to overthrow him with skulls, stage daggers and shovels.

We found a corridor at the back of the hall and got into our costumes. Once again, Edward got into an argument with Anthony. Edward said he needed room to rehearse his role as Polonius, who was a vital part of the play. Anthony said it wouldn't matter how well everyone knew their lines if they walked out with no clothes on.

I told them both to shut up and let me concentrate. I said the play wasn't called 'Polonius', and it certainly wasn't called 'Costumes'. It was called *Hamlet*. And I needed peace and quiet to look over my lines.

When it was time for the play to begin, I watched the first scene from inside the corridor. Shakespeare looked incredibly nervous as he stepped out to play the ghost. He must have been thinking about how much Ben Jonson would tease him if the king didn't like his play.

The scene ended and it was time for my mammoth performance to begin. I stepped onto the stage and didn't finish until my death scene three hours later.

I managed to remember all the words. That was something. But I was sure my performance wasn't right. Usually I have a sense of what sort of person the character is. But with Hamlet I was angry, then sad, then happy, then energetic.

I couldn't stop myself glancing at the king as he watched from under his red canopy. He was leaning on his right hand and staring at me in silence. I couldn't work out if the play had sent him into a reflective state or if he was just bored.

Finally, it was all over. The room fell into silence, and everyone turned to look at the king.

He applauded. The other noblemen joined in, and soon the whole crowd were on their feet and muttering about what a wonderful play it had been.

The king cleared his throat and the noise cut out instantly. He declared that Hamleg was

the greatest play he'd ever seen. He said that
Shakespeare had written some brilliant speeches,
and my performance had done justice to the
complicated and changeable character of Hamleg.

I nodded as though this had been exactly what
I intended. Shakespeare stepped forward and
said he was overjoyed that his unpolished lines
had pleased His Majesty, and that he would
now try to produce work that was more worthy
of such an esteemed audience. It turns out he
can fawn as well as the rest of them when he
needs to.

The king declared that we would no longer be
known as The Lord Chamberlain's Men. We
would now be known as The King's Men as
he was to become our new patron. He said we
should come back many times and perform
more of Shakespeare's wonderful tragedies.

There was more cheering and then we were led off to another huge feast. I sat next to Lawrence and managed to convince him to take on Spud as an apprentice. He was in such a good mood that he agreed right away, without complaining that he wasn't girlish enough.

After the feast, we got boats back across the river, and Lawrence was so happy he sat back and looked up at the stars instead of worrying about his priceless costumes.

Thursday 19th June

Mother and Father were very impressed when I told them the king was our new patron. Mother told me she was very proud, and then looked shocked at herself for saying something nice. We stood in awkward silence for a few minutes while Mother thought of something to complain about so everything could go back to normal.

She decided to shout at Father for never having won royal approval for anything. This gave him the terrible idea of calling himself 'The King's Shoemaker', and he asked if I could run it by the king.

It's not going to happen. The only time I'll see the king will be from the stage when I'm performing. And I've already told him how I feel about breaking away from Shakespeare's scripts to talk about footwear.

Friday 20ᵗʰ June

Lawrence wanted me and Spud to go outside Ben Jonson's window and talk about our triumph this morning.

I said we didn't need to stoop to the level of The Admiral's Men. And besides, they'll all know about our success soon enough.

They might as well change their name to 'The Second-Best Men'.

Lawrence wants us to take advantage of our new name by putting on as many plays as possible. He's going to introduce me as 'The King's Favourite' every time I go on stage. I don't know if this will build me up too much and make my performances disappointing, but I can't stop him.

I don't really mind anyway. I'll never give a performance with as much riding on it as my Hamlet in front of the king, and I feel much more relaxed about going on stage now.

I'm happy to try any role that Lawrence wants me to do, whether it's male or female, villain or hero. As long as I've got my lines and my candle, and I can block out the sound of Philip

telling me all about the great poo he's just collected, I can learn any part.

Saturday 21st June

I met Shakespeare in the tiring house this morning. He was writing frantically, so I didn't want to say anything, but he broke off to thank me for performing Hamlet so well.

I told him it was all down to his great writing, and I apologised for saying *Hamlet* wasn't as good as his other plays. Tragedy wasn't really my thing at first, but I can see why everyone likes it so much now.

Shakespeare told me not to worry and said it didn't matter because all's well that ends well.

Then he grabbed a fresh piece of paper and started scribbling away. I think he must have given himself an idea for a new play.

The End

Shakespeare and the English Theatre

This diary is set in the year 1603, when Queen Elizabeth I died, and James I became king. The early seventeenth century was a tough time for Londoners. Most of them had very little food, lived in cramped, dirty houses, and feared a deadly illness known as the plague, which returned every few years. But at least they could escape to the theatres, where some of the greatest plays ever were being performed for the first time.

Groups of actors initially travelled the countryside and performed in barns and courtyards. But some people thought they were no different from beggars, wandering around and asking for money.

To make themselves more respectable, these groups arranged for important noblemen to be their patrons. They could adopt names like 'The Admiral's Men', and in return, their patron would expect them to perform for free.

In the late sixteenth century, some of these groups constructed large buildings where they could stage plays. England's first theatres had arrived.

Having theatres created a huge demand for new plays, and writers such as Christopher Marlowe, Ben Jonson and William Shakespeare were hired to produce them.

The last of these, William Shakespeare, has become regarded as the greatest playwright of all time. His tragedies, comedies and histories are still performed all over the world.

Shakespeare had a huge influence on the English language. He coined hundreds of common words such as 'critic', 'dauntless', 'swagger', 'lonely' and 'undress', as well as phrases such as 'love is blind', 'wild goose chase', 'heart of gold', 'good riddance' and 'break the ice'. Even if you've never seen or read one of Shakespeare's plays, you've probably quoted him.

If Shakespeare had never written his plays, and if they hadn't been published after his death in the *First Folio*, the way we speak today would be different.

Shakespeare wrote for a company called The Lord Chamberlain's Men, who owned a theatre called the Globe on the south bank of the Thames. In 1603 King James I became the new patron of the company, and they changed their name to The King's Men.

London's theatres were popular in the early seventeenth century, but a group known as the Puritans soon became powerful. Puritans believed in living a simple life, based on strict religious teachings, and they regarded theatres as sinful. In 1642 the staging of plays in London was banned, bringing the first great era of English theatre to an end.

How do we know about Shakespeare?

When you look at some periods of history, it's extraordinary how much evidence has survived from so long ago. When you research into Shakespeare however, it's surprising how little we really know. There are huge gaps in our knowledge, and those who have written about him have simply had to guess at the details of his life, making their biographies as fictional as his plays.

Church records tell us when Shakespeare was born, when he was married and when he died. They also show us when his children were born, and that his son Hamnet died at the age of just 11.

We know he was making an impact on the London theatre scene by 1592, when he's referred to in the pamphlet *Groats-Worth of Wit*.

We know from legal records that he was a shareholder in The Lord Chamberlain's Men, and rich enough to buy a large property in Stratford-upon-Avon. This was unusual for a playwright, as they didn't generally make much money.

And we know from his will that he wanted his wife to have his second-best bed after he died. This might seem a little mean, but the best bed was likely to have been reserved for guests, so

the second-best one would have been the one
the couple slept in.

With so little real evidence about the life of
Shakespeare, it's no wonder so many people
have tried to work out what he was like by
studying his plays and poems. But how much
can Shakespeare's writing really tell us about
him as a person?

Unless someone stumbles across a box of
documents telling us all about Shakespeare,
we'll never know the full truth about one of
the world's greatest writers.

Timeline

1564

William Shakespeare is born in Stratford-upon-Avon. It's often said he was born on 23rd April, which is also St George's Day, but we don't know for sure if this was his real birth date.

1576

James Burbage opens the first successful playhouse of the Elizabethan era, called simply The Theatre.

1585

Shakespeare marries Anne Hathaway, but not the one who starred in *The Dark Knight Rises*. Not much is known about Shakespeare between this period and his emergence on the London theatre scene a few years later.

Timeline

1592

Robert Greene's *Groats-Worth of Wit* is published. He insults Shakespeare, calling him an 'upstart crow'. From this bizarre jibe, we know that Shakespeare was already in London and making an impact.

1593

The playwright Christopher Marlowe is killed in a fight over a bill in Deptford, South London.

1594

Shakespeare performs for Queen Elizabeth I as part of a company called The Lord Chamberlain's Men.

Timeline

1599

The Globe Theatre opens in Southwark, London. This area on the south bank of the Thames has a reputation for exciting entertainment and dangerous crime. Other attractions include cruel sports like cockfighting and bear-baiting.

1603

Queen Elizabeth I dies and James I takes the throne. He becomes the patron of the Lord Chamberlain's Men, who change their name to The King's Men.

1613

The Globe burns down after a cannon misfires during a performance of *Henry VIII*. It is rebuilt and opens again the following year.

Timeline

1616

William Shakespeare dies in Stratford-upon-Avon. As with so much about his life, we don't know exactly how he died.

1623

Thirty-six of Shakespeare's plays are published in a book that is now known as the *First Folio*. It also contained a tribute to Shakespeare written by Ben Jonson, which included the line, 'He was not of an age, but for all time'.

1642

The performance of plays is banned and most London theatres are closed.

1644

The Globe Theatre is pulled down.

| Timeline |

1970

American actor Sam Wanamaker founds the Shakespeare Globe Trust. He announces a plan to reconstruct the Globe, close to the site of the original theatre.

1997

The new Globe opens, and the first play performed is Shakespeare's *Henry V*.

Hall of fame

Shakespeare worked in a great era of English theatre, which spanned the reigns of Elizabeth I and James I. It was a remarkable time when many plays were produced that are still performed today.

James Burbage (c.1531–1597)

Actor and businessman who managed a company called The Earl of Leicester's Men. He rented land just outside the City of London and constructed a permanent building for performing plays, known as The Theatre. It was a huge success, and other playhouses followed.

Richard Burbage (1567–1619)

The son of James Burbage, Richard became the star actor in Shakespeare's company, The Lord Chamberlain's Men. He was said to have excelled in tragic roles such as Hamlet, Richard III, Othello and King Lear.

Hall of fame

Elizabeth I (1533—1603)

The last monarch of the House of Tudor, Elizabeth I reigned from 1558 until her death in 1603. The 'Elizabethan age' is famous for adventurers such as Sir Francis Drake and Sir Walter Raleigh, and playwrights such as William Shakespeare and Christopher Marlowe.

Robert Greene (1558—1592)

Playwright who was popular in his lifetime, but is now best remembered for attacking Shakespeare in his pamphlet *Groats-Worth of Wit*. Greene seems to disapprove of a mere actor like Shakespeare rising above his level and trying to compete with well-educated playwrights.

Hall of fame

James I (1566–1625)

Ruler of Scotland who became king of England and Ireland too in 1603. He was a great supporter of the theatre, and shortly after taking the throne he became the new sponsor of The Lord Chamberlain's Men, who were renamed The King's Men.

Ben Jonson (1572–1637)

Author of plays such as *The Alchemist* and *Bartholomew Fair*. Like Shakespeare, he was also an actor who achieved success as a playwright. He worked with a playing company called The Admiral's Men, who were rivals to The Lord Chamberlain's Men. As well as writing plays, he created several entertainments called 'masques' for King James I and the Queen consort.

Hall of fame

Will Kemp (died 1603)

Actor who performed with the Lord Chamberlain's Men, and was known for his physical comedy skills. He was the original performer of roles such as Dogberry in *Much Ado About Nothing*, and once Morris-danced all the way from London to Norwich over a period of nine days.

Christopher Marlowe (1564–1593)

Author of such plays as *Tamburlaine* and *The Tragical History of Doctor Faustus*. His tragedies were very successful, but his career was cut short when he was killed at the age of just 29. His work had a big influence on Shakespeare, and some researchers think the two writers sometimes collaborated. Some conspiracy theorists even believe Marlowe faked his own death and was the true author of Shakespeare's plays, and while this is quite an exciting idea, it's complete nonsense.

Hall of fame

William Shakespeare **(1564–1616)**
Author of *Hamlet, King Lear, Romeo and Juliet, Macbeth, Othello* and many other famous plays. He was the greatest English playwright, and perhaps the greatest writer who ever lived. It's easy to be put off when someone tells you something is the best ever, because you want to make up your own mind. But if you go and see a good production of one of Shakespeare's plays, you might become a fan too.

John Webster **(c.1580–c.1634)**
Writer of gloomy tragedies *The White Devil* and *The Duchess of Malfi*. Although his plays fell out of favour in the 18th and 19th centuries, he became popular again in the 20th century, and his two major works are still regularly performed today.

Shakespeare plays mentioned in Robert's diary

Anthony and Cleopatra

Tragedy about the doomed romance between Mark Anthony of Rome and Cleopatra of Egypt.

As You Like It

Comedy in which the heroine Rosalind seeks refuge in the Forest of Arden. Contains the well-known speech 'All the world's a stage'.

The Comedy of Errors

The shortest of Shakespeare's surviving plays, this is a story of mistaken identity involving two sets of identical twins.

Hamlet

Prince Hamlet of Denmark seeks revenge against his father's murderer in this classic tragedy full of famous speeches.

Shakespeare plays mentioned
in Robert's diary

Henry V

A play about the 15th-century English king
that revolves around the Battle of Agincourt
and contains many famous speeches.

Henry VI Part 1

Part of a trilogy set in 15th-century England
which shows the struggle for the English
throne in the War of the Roses.

Julius Caesar

Tragedy set in Ancient Rome about the
political struggles leading to the assassination
of Caesar.

King Lear

Tragedy in which an elderly king attempts to
divide up his land between his three daughters,
and descends into madness and despair.

Shakespeare plays mentioned in Robert's diary

Measure for Measure

The Duke of Vienna disguises himself so he can walk unnoticed among his citizens. He hands power over to his strict deputy, who tries to enforce the death penalty.

The Merchant of Venice

A rich moneylender called Shylock agrees a loan to a young merchant called Antonio on the condition that he'll remove a pound of his flesh if he can't pay it back.

Shakespeare plays mentioned in Robert's diary

The Merry Wives of Windsor

Comedy in which Shakespeare brought back a popular character from earlier plays called Sir John Falstaff, who pretends to woo two wealthy married women to get their money.

A Midsummer Night's Dream

Comedy about four lovers and a troupe of actors who encounter fairies in an enchanted forest.

Much Ado about Nothing

Comedy about two sets of lovers, Claudio and Hero and Benedick and Beatrice. The latter playfully argue before admitting their love, and can be seen as the forerunners of couples in modern romantic comedies.

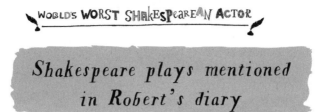

Shakespeare plays mentioned in Robert's diary

Romeo and Juliet

Tragedy about a boy and girl who fall in love despite the conflict between their families, the Montagues and Capulets.

The Taming of the Shrew

Comedy set in Verona in which Petruchio woos a bad-tempered woman called Katherine.

The Tempest

Prospero, the former Duke of Milan, and his daughter Miranda live on an island with a savage creature called Caliban and a spirit called Ariel. Prospero conjures up a storm to shipwreck his brother Antonio on the island.

Shakespeare plays mentioned in Robert's diary

Titus Andronicus

Roman general Titus takes revenge on Tamora, the Queen of the Goths, in Shakespeare's most violent tragedy.

The Two Gentlemen of Verona

Romantic comedy about two friends called Proteus and Valentine who fall in love with the same woman, Silvia.

Glossary

Ague
A fever caused by malaria, often marked by shivering and pain in the bones.

Apprentice
A trainee who works for free in exchange for learning a skill.

Bear-baiting
A cruel sport in which a bear is chained to a post and killed by dogs. Henry VIII and Elizabeth I were both said to be fond of this 'entertainment'.

Canopy
A fancy cloth covering suspended over something such as a throne or bed.

Cockfighting
A nasty sport in which two cockerels fight to the death in front of a crowd.

Comedy
One of the three categories of Shakespeare's plays in the *First Folio*. Comedies have a light-hearted tone and feature happy endings, often involving marriage. Shakespeare's comedies include *A Midsummer Night's Dream, Much Ado About Nothing* and *All's Well That Ends Well*.

Company
A group of actors who perform together.

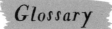

Glossary

Coronation
A ceremony in which someone becomes king or queen.

Doublet
A tight-fitting jacket that was popular in the Elizabethan era.

Elizabethan
From the reign of Elizabeth I, which began in 1558 and ended in 1603.

Farthingale
A large, hooped cage worn under a skirt to give it a wide, circular shape.

First Folio
The name given to the collection of Shakespeare's plays published in 1623. Its actual title was *Mr William Shakespeare's Comedies, Histories and Tragedies*.

Gallery
A raised area in a theatre with seats. You had to pay extra to get into the gallery at the Globe, and even more if you wanted a cushion.

Glossary

Groundlings
People who watched plays from the ground, which was the cheapest area of a theatre.

History
One of the three categories of Shakespeare's plays in the *First Folio*. Histories bring important past events to life, and usually focus on struggles for power. Shakespeare's histories include *Richard III* and the three parts of *Henry VI*.

Jacobean
From the reign of James I, which began in 1603 and ended in 1625.

Masque
A type of performance that was popular in the 16th and 17th centuries and combined music, dancing and acting with elaborate sets.

Nobleman
A man who belongs to the highest social class.

Glossary

Pageant
An outdoor procession
of people in colourful
costumes, usually to
celebrate a person
or event.

Patron
A rich person who
helps to pay for the
work of an individual
or group in return for
their work or services.
Queen Elizabeth I
and King James I
were both patrons
of Shakespeare's
acting company.

Pit
The standing area on
the floor of a theatre,
where those who paid
a penny could watch
the performance.

Plague
A deadly disease
that broke out
several times during
the Elizabethan
and Jacobean
eras. Thousands
of Londoners were
killed by it, and it was
thought to be God's
way of punishing
sinners. We now know
it was spread by fleas.

Player
A term for an actor
that was used in
Shakespeare's day.

Props
Objects needed for
use in a play, such
as swords, daggers,
bottles and crowns.

Glossary

Puritans
A strict religious group which thought that pleasures like going to plays were sinful.

Queen consort
The wife of a ruling king. Anne of Denmark was the queen consort of England, Ireland and Scotland from 1603 to 1619.

Ruff
A lace collar worn by both men and women in the Elizabethan and Jacobean eras. They became a symbol of wealth and status.

Tiring house
A small room at the back of the stage where props and costumes were kept. It was known as the 'tiring house' because it was where the actors put on their attire.

Tragedy
One of the three categories of Shakespeare's plays in the *First Folio*. Tragedies are generally serious plays with disastrous events and unhappy endings. Shakespeare's tragedies include *Macbeth*, *Hamlet* and *King Lear*.

Wherry
A rowing boat used to carry passengers along a river.

THE LONG-LOST
SECRET DIARY OF THE
WORLD'S WORST

Shortlisted for the
Lancashire School Library Service
Fantastic Book Awards (FBA) 2017–18.

'Although easy to read, the vocabulary is
great and the plot lines engaging – excellent
reads for developing readers.'
Library Girl and Book Boy Blog

PB ISBN: 978-1-912233-19-9

PB ISBN: 978-1-912233-20-5

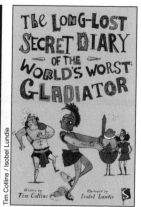

PB ISBN: 978-1-912537-26-6

PB ISBN: 978-1-912006-67-0

PB ISBN: 978-1-912006-66-3

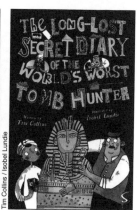

PB ISBN: 978-1-912537-44-0

A selected list of Scribo titles

The prices shown below are correct at the time of going to press. However, The Salariya Book Company reserves the right to show new retail prices on covers, which may differ from those previously advertised.

Gladiator School by Dan Scott

1	Blood Oath	978-1-908177-48-3	£6.99
2	Blood & Fire	978-1-908973-60-3	£6.99
3	Blood & Sand	978-1-909645-16-5	£6.99
4	Blood Vengeance	978-1-909645-62-2	£6.99
5	Blood & Thunder	978-1-910184-20-2	£6.99
6	Blood Justice	978-1-910184-43-1	£6.99

Shivers by John Townsend

1	Ghost Stories	978-1-912233-52-6	£6.99
2	Pirate Stories	978-1-912233-51-9	£6.99

Scarlet Hood by Mark Evans

978-1-912233-34-2	£7.99

Ballet School by Fiona Macdonald

1. Peter & The Wolf   978-1-911242-37-6 £6.99
2. Samira's Garden   978-1-912006-62-5 £6.99

The Curse of the Speckled Monster
   by John Townsend

1 Graverobbers & Gallows   978-1-912233-32-8 £6.99
2 The Twist of the Hangman 978-1-912233-33-5 £6.99

The Shakespeare Plot by Alex Woolf

1 Assassin's Code   978-1-911242-38-3 £9.99
2 The Dark Forest   978-1-912006-95-3 £9.99
3 The Powder Treason   978-1-912006-33-5 £9.99

Visit our website at:

www.salariya.com

All Scribo and Salariya Book Company titles can be
ordered from your local bookshop, or by post from:

The Salariya Book Co. Ltd,
25 Marlborough Place
Brighton
BN1 1UB